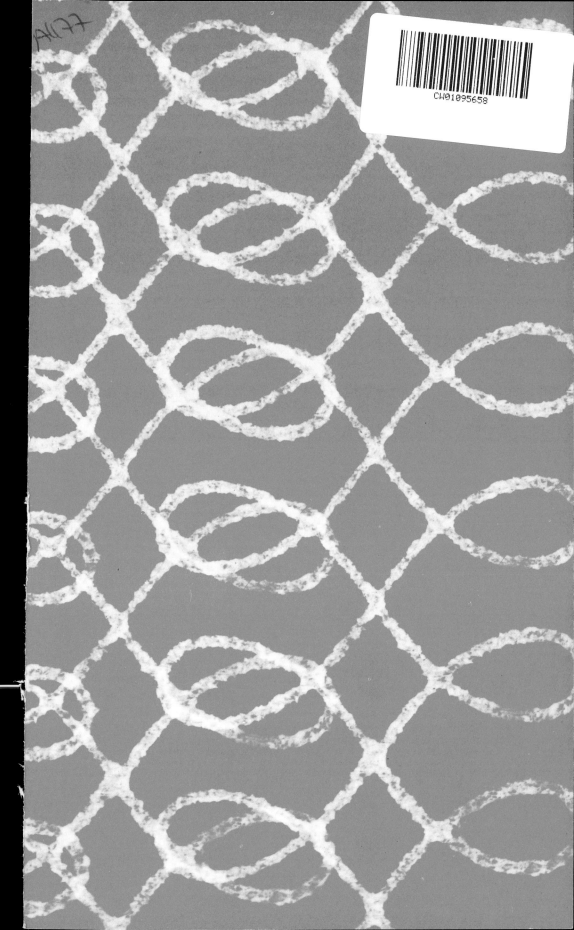

FLOWERS
&
FLOURISHES

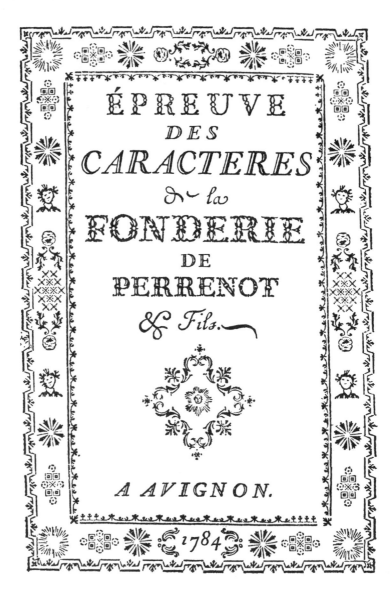

ÉPREUVE
DES
CARACTERES
& la
FONDERIE
DE
PERRENOT
& Fils.

A AVIGNON.

1784

Title-page of Perrenot et Fils
specimen of 1784

Flowers
&
Flourishes

INCLUDING A
NEWLY ANNOTATED EDITION OF
A Suite of Fleurons

JOHN RYDER

THE BODLEY HEAD
FOR MACKAYS

Printed and bound in Great Britain
at their works at Lordswood, Chatham
by W & J Mackay Ltd
and published by The Bodley Head Ltd
9 Bow Street, London, WC2E 7AL
The design of the index pages
and the type founders' display
pages are by Yvonne Skargon
the photographic section
is by John Preston Bell
The text paper
is Basingwerk Parchment
made by Grosvenor Chater

CONTENTS

FLOWERS
&
FLOURISHES

This showing of all the flowers, decorations, ornaments and rules held at the printing house of Mackays has been prepared to mark the centenary of their foundation.

Most of the flowers in this *Index* are metal types made and cast in the same way as letters. Their production was a natural development from the flowers cut in brass as binders' stamps and many of them were designed, just as binders' stamps had been, to build up into arabesque patterns.

The earliest example of printers' flowers appeared in a Veronese imprint of 1478—*Dell'arte de ben morire by* Cardinal Capranica (page 8). Although these flowers are usually attributed to the printers Giovanni and Alberto Alvise it is probable, points out Giovanni Mardersteig, that Felice Feliciano was also involved with the printing of Cardinal Capranica's book. These flowers appear in earlier mss of Feliciano and in later books printed by him.

When one looks at the decorated bindings of fifteenth- and sixteenth-century books the origin of a great many sixteenth-century printers' flowers becomes obvious. The image of the flower was, of course, also *in* the paper in the form of watermarks (see page 9). But because the filigree technique of making watermark images is so different from

❖❖❖ ARTE ❖❖❖ DE BEN ❖❖❖ MORI RE

Felice Feliciano's flowers

the technique of engraving a binders' stamp (which is so similar to the technique of engraving a printers' flower) the design of watermarks has little in common with either the stamps or the types of the same period.

A repertoire of robust flowers appeared in the sixteenth century and it included some fine arabesques which could be made up from several units. Perhaps the most famous of these, and one which has been in constant use ever since, is Granjon's arabesque of about 1565. Another of similar antiquity was comparatively neglected until specially re-cut by Monotype in 1956 for *A Suite of Fleurons*. This, too, may have been originally designed and cut by Granjon and was re-cut at my instigation.

During the seventeenth century many flowers were re-cut in an inferior manner. But in the eighteenth century the re-cutting of traditional fleuron designs was refined and many beautiful examples were done by Fournier, Baskerville and Bodoni. Especially Fournier and Bodoni produced splendid specimen books of their work (pages 14 & 15), and

[8]

*Flowers as watermarks in the fifteenth century (above)
and sixteenth century (below)*

they had many imitators as the specimen of Perrenot of 1784 shows (see frontispiece).

Before the beginning of the nineteenth century 'flowers' had already extended their image. On page 18 you can see 'soldiers as flowers' arranged in a specimen book from the Imprenta Real at Madrid, 1799. Of course acorns and fists

Japanese handprinted decorative paper

as pointers have been in common use since the sixteenth century, but during the nineteenth century typefounders offered ships, houses, trains, birds, animals, fishes all in great variety. But it must be regretted that when the traditional flowers and arabesques were re-cut by Victorian hands they became attenuated and characterless forms. The twentieth-century re-cuttings for the Monotype have done much to restore the balance and yet the experiments of this

Letters of the Grot R alphabet arranged
by Michael Harvey

century cannot be rated highly, at least not experiments like the one which gave us Glint ornaments.

There are now far too many different designs available and it rests with the printer to select and try to keep his repertoire within bounds. Despite the Monotype's great range, when I last showed an interest in flowers, in 1956, I asked for a few additions. Firstly there was the 'Fournier' star to go with the bubble as a strip ornament (✳✧✳), then the arabesque mentioned above, and also a finely shaped diamond ⬦ dating back to a Vincent Figgins specimen of 1815.

The traditional uses of flowers will always be needed to reproduce the image of a particular period in typography and if the original is properly examined and sensitively transcribed the effect can be very convincing. Such traditional uses are as markers, pointers, paragraph markers and line fillers, hiatus marks, title-page borders, bands of decoration, and so on. All of these examples extend back to the fifteenth century as printers' types. The fist as a pointer, for instance, sometimes looked upon as a vulgar modern device, was discreetly used at Strassburg in 1498 in an edition of *Horace* by Johann Gruninger.

Maybe the most distinguished, traditional use of flowers lies in specimen books produced by the typefounders themselves. Certainly Bodoni's *Fregi e Majuscole*, printed by him at Parma in 1771 (pages 14 & 15) has a special quality, but let us examine possible new uses to which this material might be put.

Adequately cast lead types have obviously had their own influence on the ways in which they can be used. Whilst printing is done directly from these squarely fitting pieces of metal the patterns of design are limited by certain physical

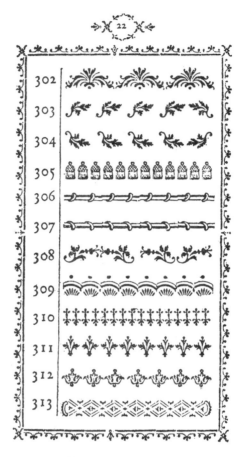

BODONI: *Fregi e Majuscole, Parma 1771*

factors. But with the addition of photography the traditional look can be adjusted simply by altering focus and
scale. The example on page 19 shows a border unit I made
for Stellar Press. The original is from a title-page woodcut
device made by Eustachio Celebrino for Donatus' *De octo
oratonis partibus* printed at Perugia in 1517. Celebrino
graduated as a double doctor from Padua University in

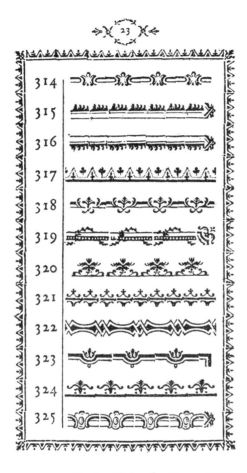

BODONI: *Fregi e Majuscole, Parma 1771*

philosophy and medicine but preferred to work as a free-lance engraver and his work for Arrighi is well-known. Thus the design is wholly traditional but we see it here printed just out of focus.

This pattern was made for a Bodley Head cover-paper, and variations could be devised by changing scale in the two lines of flowers or by using three lines of flowers. The focus could be different in each line and colour changes may be explored endlessly.

Massive enlargement of a single fleuron (or part of a fleuron), and overprinting the same image in another orientation in another colour could be the basis of a new range of experiments. Or a simple flower like this diamond ◄❖► might be redrawn and combined with other drawn symbols to produce cover/wrapping paper of such quality as the Japanese example on page 10.

Nicolas Langlois, Architecture à la Mode,
Paris, c.1705

Seventeenth-century decorated initial
in use at Oxford in 1674

In a wider sense than is implicit in changes of focus and scale, photography is one possible answer to presenting flowers in a new light. We have been experimenting photographically with flower units printed on transparent material, backed by reflective surfaces such as prisms and cubes. The angle of the camera lens or of the transparent surface adds another dimension of change.

Since, in the printer's language, *flowers* include such abstract shapes as triangles, squares, circles, multiple rules curved or straight, there is no reason in the present context why we should not include abstract shapes like letters, Roman, Greek and all the exotic alphabets and even include hieroglyphs and cuniform characters. Thus, the example of letters as flowers arranged by Michael Harvey in Grot R characters on page 12 may prove an interesting lead. Not that this is in any way new. Many examples are in use and recently a particularly successful one was made for Jaeger

shops using Clarendon capital letters joining and over-
lapping. Light brown letters were printed on a darker
brown background.

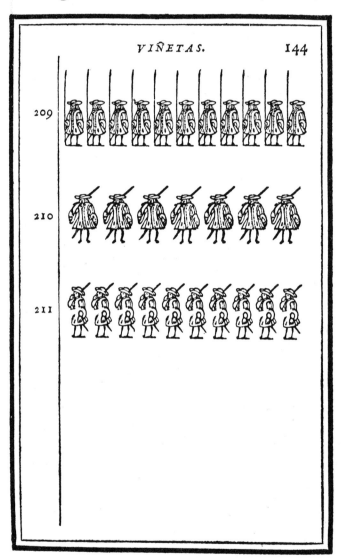

Soldiers as flowers from the Imprenta Real, Madrid, 1799

The Celebrino border unit enlarged and printed out of focus

Eighteenth-century French book decoration
engraved on wood

Having turned to photographic aids the sources of supply are obviously far greater than the combined repertoires of all contemporary typefounders. The sources of supply of flowers, fleurons, vignettes, flourishes, rules, decorations, arabesques are unlimited. The flowers on page 16 come from a French book of engraved decorations prepared by Nicolas Langlois and published in Paris at the end of the seventeenth century.

BRASS.

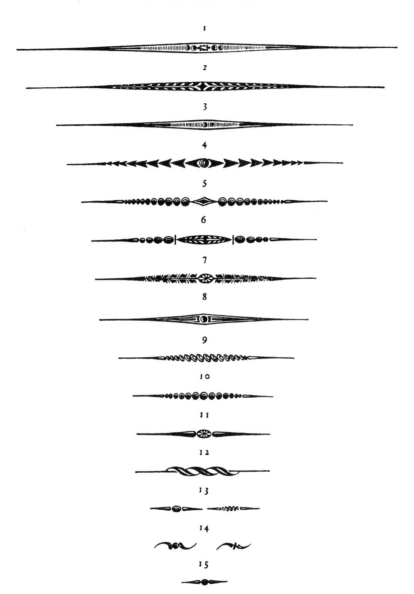

A page from S. E. C. Stephenson's sale catalogue of 1797

The flowered letter which accompanies this example is in use today at the University Press, Oxford and its style dates back to Ratdolt in Venice at the end of the fifteenth century. Although the letter itself may have come from sixteenth-century Amsterdam its origin may be traced back from Holland to Antwerp (Plantin), to Paris (Geofroy Tory and the great sixteenth-century French printers), and back to fifteenth-century Venice.

There are many sources of inspiration waiting to be explored. For instance the ceramic tiles on the façade of a Mexican church (page 11) may be just the twist needed for an inspired new look at flowers on the printed page. Or if one is looking for a lesser known decorated swelled rule to provide an interesting flourish, with the aid of a camera we may select from earlier examples as from the collection shown on page 21. Or engraved book decorations of the eighteenth century may provide an answer (page 20).

The photographic experiments shown between pages 153–168 are by John Preston Bell who, with a handful of printers' flowers, a camera and an enlarger, has opened the door on a fresh look at these familiar images. The precise typographic impressions from metal flowers are completely altered when much enlarged details and mirror images are shown. Further changes come easily from the arrangement of negative and positive printings and overprints, colour changes, and the setting of backgrounds in sympathy or in contrast by content or by colour.

This encouragement to use decoration should be accompanied by a warning. So many printed pages are ruined by underdeveloped designers putting their marks on the title-pages and chapter openings with an inappropriate flower. Restraint is the first and highest canon of typographic practice. The designer's fist must always remain invisible. A certain quality will then become entirely his own and eventually his imprint 'appears' with subtlety.   J.R.

THE
INDEX

American
Type Founders

Civilité Ornaments

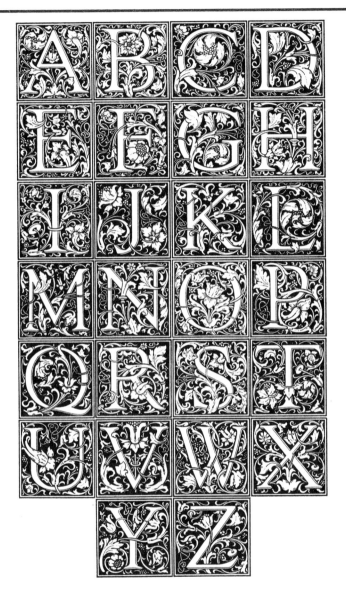

Cloister Initials 60 Point

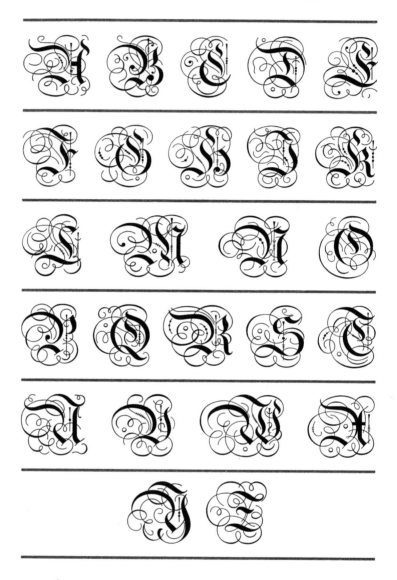

Dutch Initials 48 Point

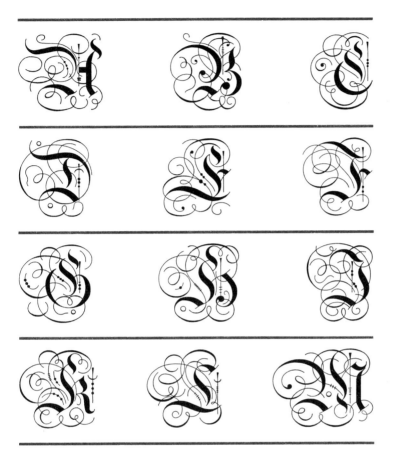

Dutch Initials 60 Point

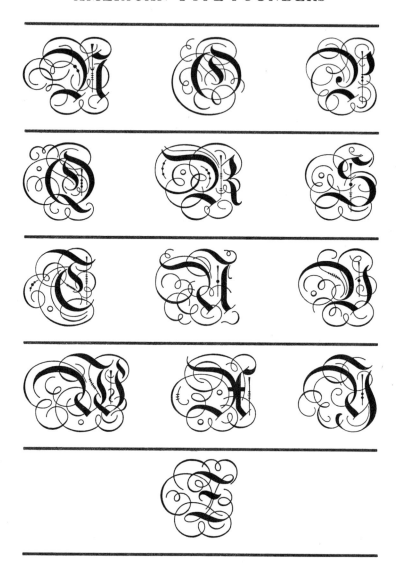

Dutch Initials 60 Point

3601 Troyer 36 Point

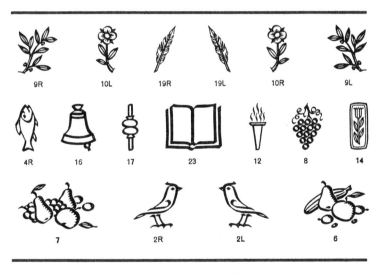

3602 Troyer 36 Point

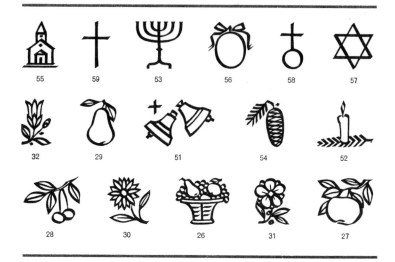

3603 Troyer 36 Point

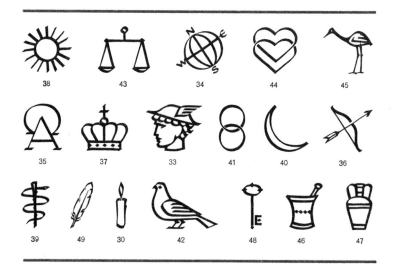

3604 Troyer 36 Point

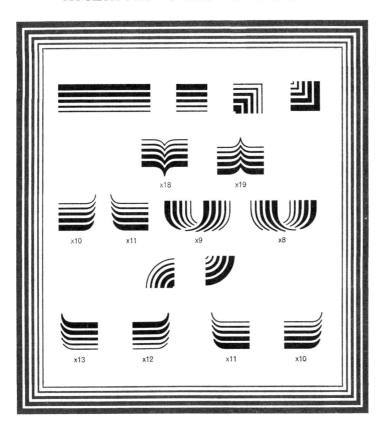

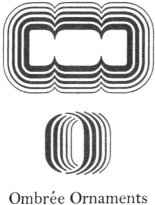

Ombrée Ornaments

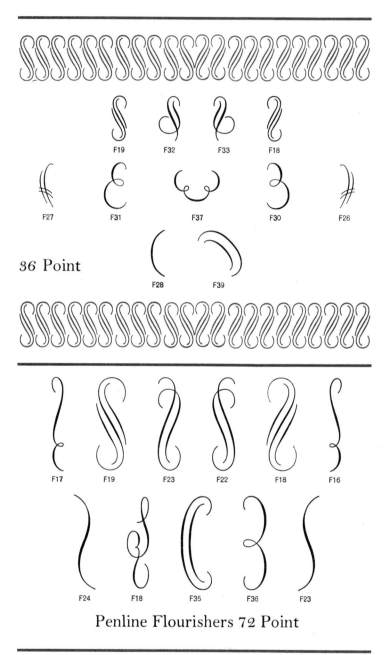

F19   F32   F33   F18

F27   F31   F37   F30   F26

36 Point

F28   F39

F17   F19   F23   F22   F18   F16

F24   F18   F35   F36   F23

Penline Flourishers 72 Point

Amsterdam
Typefoundry

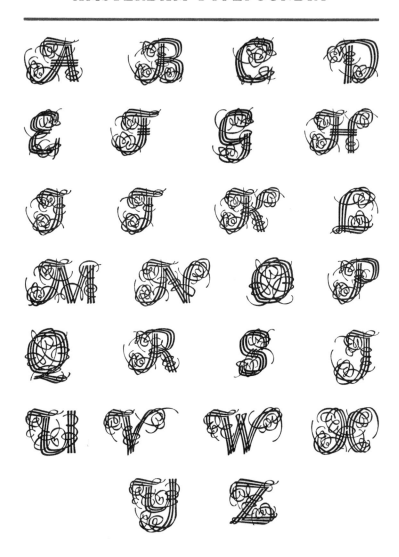

Raffia Initials

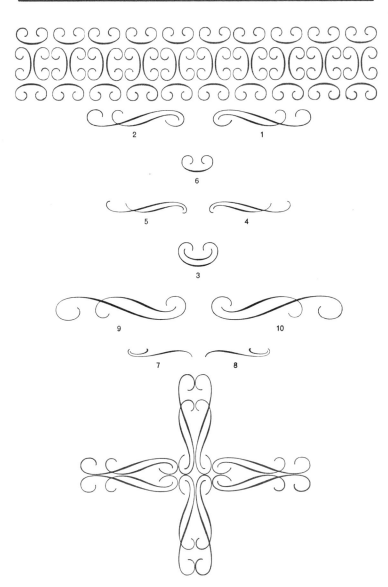

Gracia Ornaments

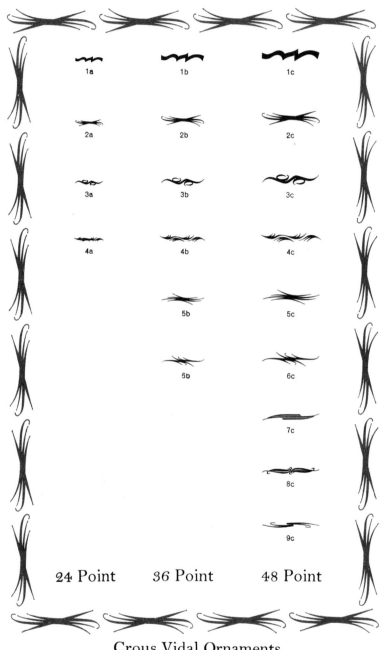

1a   1b   1c

2a   2b   2c

3a   3b   3c

4a   4b   4c

5b   5c

6b   6c

7c

8c

9c

24 Point   36 Point   48 Point

Crous Vidal Ornaments

72 Point

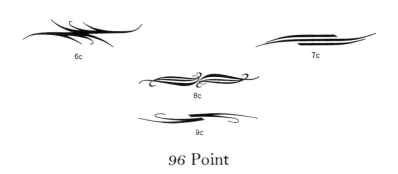

96 Point

Crous Vidal Ornaments

| 158 | 159 | 160 | 164 | 165 | 169 | 174 | 177 | 179 |

12 Point Primula Ornaments

Bauer
Typefoundry

BAUER TYPEFOUNDRY

6 Point

| 4039 | 4040 | 3861 | 3862 | 4009-10 | 4011 | 3917 | 3916 |

9 Point

| 4068 | 4069 | 4080 | 4081 | 4144 | 4145 |

12 Point

| 4214 | 4215 | 4237 | 4283 | 4284 |

| 4294 | 4292 | 4293 | 4308 | 4306 | 4307 | 4311 | 4309 | 4310 |

18 Point

| 4322 | 4366 | 4367 |

24 Point

4410

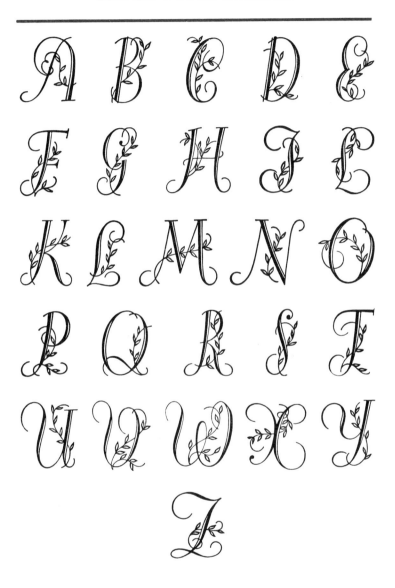

Maria Ballé Initials 54 Point

BAUER TYPEFOUNDRY

Bernhard Cursive Ornaments Series 1

Bernhard Cursive Ornaments Series 1

Bernhard Cursive Ornaments Series 2

Bernhard Cursive Ornaments Series 2

TYPE

Fry's Baskerville

DECORATION

Bauer Bernhard Cursive

A HISTORY OF
Copperplate

MACKAY
1971

Berthold
Typefoundry

4 Point

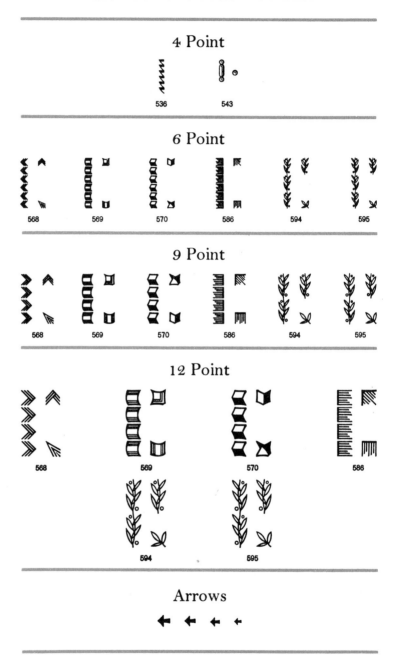

536   543

6 Point

568   569   570   586   594   595

9 Point

568   569   570   586   594   595

12 Point

568   569   570   586

594   595

Arrows

Haas
Typefoundry

HAAS TYPEFOUNDRY

10 Point

2917   2918   2920   2921   2922   2924   2925

12 Point

2929   2930   2935   2936   2942   2943   2944   8074   8075

18 Point

2957   2958   2958

24 Point

2965   2966   2969   2970   2973   2974

2975   2976   2977   2979   2980

36 Point

2991   2992   3196   3504

48 Point

2997

2996

2994   2995   8035

8036   8078   8079

TYPE
Fry's Baskerville
DECORATION
Haas 3196 & 3504

TWENTIETH CENTURY VERSE

AN ANTHOLOGY

Volume One

TYPE
Walbaum

DECORATION
Haas 3196
(reverse line block)

An Anthology of
Twentieth
Century Verse

VOLUME ONE

WHAT
MASIE
KNEW

Henry James

BODLEY HEAD
LONDON

TYPE
Scotch Roman

DECORATION
Haas 2957

The second parting from Miss Overmore had been bad enough, but this first parting from Mrs. Wix was much worse. The child had lately been to the dentist's and had a term of comparison for the screwed-up intensity of the scene. It was dreadfully silent, as it had been when her tooth was taken out; Mrs. Wix had on that occasion grabbed her hand and they had clung to each other with the frenzy of their determination not to scream. Maisie, at the dentist's, had been heroically still, but just when she felt most anguish had become aware of an audible shriek on the part of her companion, a spasm of stifled sympathy. This was reproduced by the only sound that broke their supreme embrace when, a month later, the "arrangement", as her periodical uprootings were called, played the part of the horrible forceps. Embedded in Mrs. Wix's nature as her tooth had been socketed in her gum, the operation of extracting her would really have been a case for chloroform. It was a hug that fortunately left nothing to say, for the poor woman's want of words at such an hour seemed to fall in with her want of everything. Maisie's alternate parent, in the outermost vestibule—he liked the impertinence of crossing as much as that of his late wife's threshold—stood over them with his open watch and his still more open grin, while from the only corner

135

TYPE

Fry's Baskerville

DECORATION

Haas 2996 & 2997
(and centre of 2997, modified
and enlarged, line block)

Haas'sche
Typefoundry

INVITE YOU TO
THEIR STAND

TYPES
Rosart and
Plantin

DECORATION
Stevens, Shanks
(enlarged, reversed, line block)

THE
WHITE HORSE
BOOKSHOP

MARLBOROUGH

The Monotype Corporation

6 Point

3	—	82	
21		83	
23		87	
33	▼	94	
41		102	
43		103	●
45	◀	120	•••
56		121	
57		145	
60		466	
68		479	
78	■	482	
79	□	483	
81	‖‖		

8 Point

7		82	
23		83	
24		84	
29	◆	92	
43		136	
65		255	
66		479	
78	■	483	
79	□		

10 Point

23		204	
24		223	
42		248	
56		265	
65		280	
66		318	
103		480	
188		1283	
202		3288	

12 Point

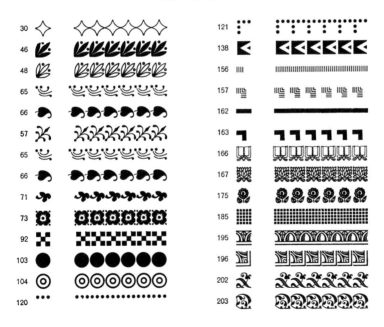

30		121	
46		138	
48		156	
65		157	
66		162	
57		163	
65		166	
66		167	
71		175	
73		185	
92		195	
103		196	
104		202	
120		203	

12 Point continued

204		281		
205		284		
206		288		
207		318		
208		329		
209		330		
216		463		
217		467		
219		468		
224		469		
230		470		
231		480		
248		482		
249		484		
254		652		
255		1127		
257		1129		
258		1309		
261		1338		
262		1341		
267		1429		
276		1449		
277		1450		
280		1451		

14 Point

18 Point

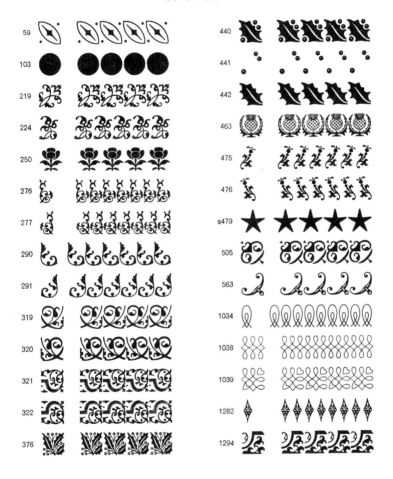

TYPE
Caslon

DECORATION
Mono 224

The Comedies & Tragedies of William Shakespeare

Complete and unabridged with notes & glossary

LONDON &
NEW YORK

18 Point continued

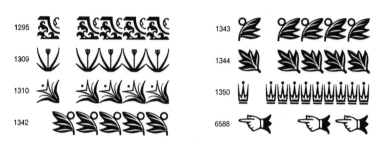

24 Point

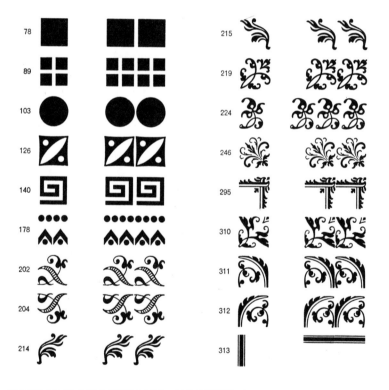

24 Point continued

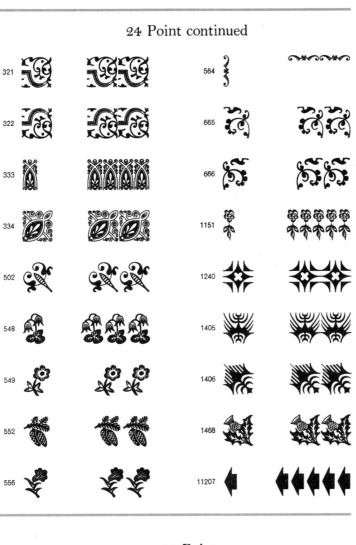

30 Point

36 Point

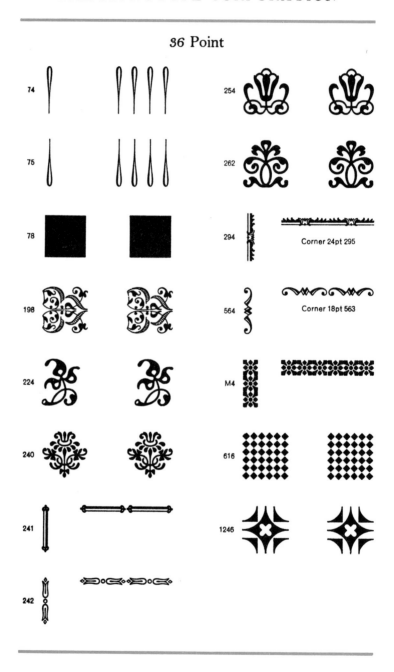

74

75

78

198

224

240

241

242

254

262

294   Corner 24pt 295

564   Corner 18pt 563

M4

616

1246

Stempel
Typefoundry

STEMPEL TYPEFOUNDRY

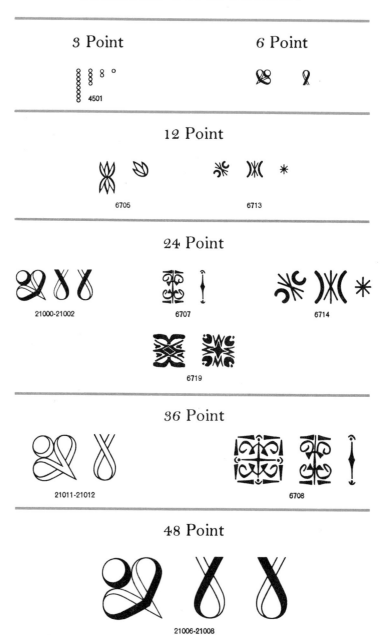

3 Point

4501

6 Point

12 Point

6705   6713

24 Point

21000-21002   6707   6714

6719

36 Point

21011-21012   6708

48 Point

21006-21008

Stephenson
Blake

STEPHENSON BLAKE

6 Point

59c   59c   53c

8 Point

555   555

12 Point

7   25c   78c   78c   79c   388/395   391/436   391/436   392/436a   393/513

14 Point

351/29c   351/29c   354/531   355/531a   357/567   357/567   840

18 Point

329/54c   331/63c   343/435a   343/435a   342/435

347/528   347/528   349/571   349/571   524   524   525

526   348   330/55c   328/50c   73c   74c   75c

STEPHENSON BLAKE

24 Point

315/68c   315/68c   315/68c   326/502   326/502

12c   69c   69c

30 Point

311/522   311/522   51c   51c   69c   69c

36 Point

7c   7c   12c   12c

42 Point

306/420c   306/420c

48 Point

305/570

305/570

305/570

304/521

304/521

304/521

60 Point

17

303/14c

303/14c

15c

15c

72 Point

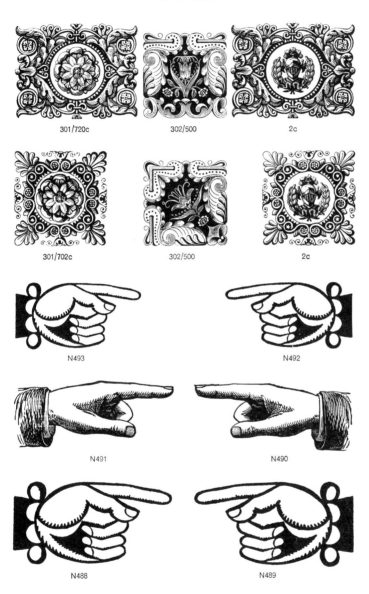

301/720c   302/500   2c

301/702c   302/500   2c

N493   N492

N491   N490

N488   N489

Stevens, Shanks Typefoundry

Consort, Thorne Shaded,
Marina Script, Thorogood,
Scotch Roman, Erhardt,

American Type Founders
Penline Flourishers
Stevens Shanks
Ship 3

NO DELAY IN LOADING

LIDDEN & SUTTON

FOR

San Francisco

MAGNIFICENT SHIP

WITCHCRAFT

CUTHBERT SKARGON Commander

is now rapidly loading at PIER II, E.R

for freight apply to

LIDDEN & SUTTON

114 Pearl Street

TYPES
Rosart and
Plantin

DECORATION
Stevens, Shanks
(enlarged, reversed, line block)

THE
WHITE HORSE
BOOKSHOP

MARLBOROUGH

You are invited to inspect our stock of books
New & Secondhand

24 Point

30 Point

36 Point

3   1   2

12 Point   24 Point   30 Point

Type Ornaments

Rules

PLAIN RULES

R19 SHADED

R22 SHADED

R96 SHADED

FINE

MEDIUM

DOUBLE MEDIUM

1 PT

1½ PT

2 PT

3 PT

6 PT

[94]

DECORATED & SWELLED RULES

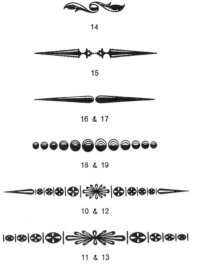

14

15

16 & 17

18 & 19

10 & 12

11 & 13

STEVENS, SHANKS

KLINGSPOR

04

05

06

07

08

09

DECORATED & SWELLED RULES

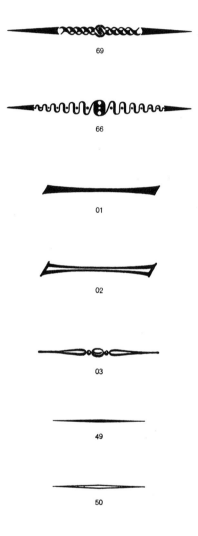

69

66

01

02

03

49

50

6 & 7

MONOTYPE

Third impression
revised in
the author's
hand, 1975

ANDREAE
ALTHAMERI
BRENZII

Annotationes in Epistolam
beati I·A C O B I
iamprimum editae.

' , '

Cum Indice.

**Argentorati apud Ioannem
Schottum.** 1 5 2 7.

....

*A certain need of decoration
expressed in commas*

Curiously, Frederic Warde's book
<u>Printers Ornaments</u> published by
Monotype in 1928 had a minute
hiatus decoration on the title-pa
of 3 dots arranged so: ∴

A SUITE OF

FLEURONS

OR

A Preliminary Enquiry
*into the history & combinable
natures of certain printers'
flowers conducted by*
JOHN RYDER

PHOENIX HOUSE LTD
LONDON

Several variant bindings have
appeared & a small edition
was published under Tinlings
imprint. The book was
sponsored by Philip Evans.

Third impression
revised in
the author's
hand, 1975

Revised 1975
© John Ryder 1975

PRINTED IN GREAT BRITAIN
First published 1956

CONTENTS

All the working papers,
layouts, proofs of this
little book which
were made at the
Miniature Press,
Richmond, are now
deposited at the
Bodleian Library,
Oxford.

ACKNOWLEDGMENT

To Stanley Morison and Sir Francis Meynell for their researches and expositions this present enquiry owes a great debt.

The path of production has not been entirely smooth. At an early stage, but for some kindly acts by Mr L. E. Williams of the Monotyping Service Ltd, the frustration of delay might have led to an impasse. And most sincere thanks to Tinlings of Liverpool for so very ably seeing this small but complicated job through their composing, machining and binding workshops.

Other encouragements, material aids and information have been given freely by John Baker, Dr Konrad Bauer, William Turner Berry, Harry Carter, Michael Chater, Geoffrey Dowding, John Dreyfus, Rudolph Hostettler, M. B. B. Nijkerk, Dr Ovink, Walter Tracy, Dr Voet, Beatrice Warde, Berthold Wolpe, and Hermann Zapf.

June 1956   J.R.

For
Tinlings of
Liverpool
read
Philip Evans
of Kinton

[7]

These flowers have been
re-cut & used by
Dr Giovanni Mardersteig.
They also appeared in
the Veronese edition of
Aesop, 1479, of which
the Officina Bodoni
has made a reproduction.
Mardersteig has shown
that these 8 flowers
were probably the work
of Felice Feliciano.

INTRODUCTION

THE BROTHERS Giovanni and Alberto Aluise printed Capranica's *Arte de ben morire* (Verona, 1478) in which the following printers' flowers appeared:

❖🏵🌸❖ ARTE ❖🏵🌸❖
DE BEN 🌸❖🌸 MORIRE

Mr Ivins of the Metropolitan Museum, New York, drew attention to this example which may be the original use of decorative printing types. Since that time many flowers have been cut and recut and the story of their use and abuse, of their flourishing and falling into disrepute and of their sufferings under successions of fashion has yet to be told. The scale of the present work forbids any detailed history or application even of the few flowers it treats. And yet in the following pages there may be found a basis on which to build a larger suite and at the same time certain fundamental principles of the design and arrangement of these flowers will emerge.

The historical notes are tentative although, as may be appreciated from the Acknowledgments, some trouble has been taken to bring the researches of eminent persons to bear

[9]

upon this obscure subject. The mainspring of the problem arises from the fact that so little valuable information on the work of the early punchcutters (Robert Granjon, for instance) exists—often no specimens of any sort have survived. For instance there does not seem to be any positive evidence that Claude Garamond cut a single punch for decorative material. And again: what part did Bernard Salomon play in the production of typographic arabesques? Until a clearer picture of the work of Garamond, Granjon, Le Bé, Sabon and other punchcutters of this period can be established surmise and intelligent guesses will have to be tolerated.

The more distant origins of printers' flowers are somewhat vague in detail. Collections of arabesque patterns culled from the decorated material, manuscripts and other articles imported from the East were published in Italy, Switzerland, France, Germany, Holland and England in the first half of the sixteenth century and used as models by wood-engravers and makers of binders' stamps. In turn these binders' stamps have served as models for punchcutters.

In the last section the origin of certain diamond-shaped flowers is reasonably traced to binders' stamps but, if space would permit, an interesting digression might be carried into the National Gallery where, on dress material depicted in Crivelli's 'Immaculate Conception',

[10]

The long-awaited work of Giovanni Mardersteig on the punch-cutter, Griffo, may prove of interest here.

Bodoni, Holland Press, 1960
Fournier, Eu granunia Press, 1965
Lamesle, Hertzberger, 1965

1492, may be seen both the naturalistic pine-apple and a stylised flower within a diamond of fair shape.

The early forms of flowers that may be bought from typefoundries of the present day have survived periods of bastard recutting. It has so often happened that immediately a skilful punchcutter produces fine, sensitive designs along come the imitators with nothing in their hands and hearts but the desire to cash in and make profit. The flowers of Fournier were badly recut many times and little wonder that he (Fournier) almost rejoiced to see Bodoni's finely executed copies. Sometimes the imitators, by making much use of certain ornaments, have come to be regarded as originators. A good case in point are the favourite flowers of Baskerville who recut them with some skill after Rosart who had in turn recut them after Fournier.

Original size may be a factor of importance. Some designs, available through Monotype, have been cut in a range of sizes from 6 to 36pt. The smallest size may appear too complicated and fussy whilst the largest size may appear too simple a shape for the weight of ink it carries. Certainly Fournier's flower (MONOTYPE 475-6) does not look well either in its smallest or largest sizes.

The total number of flower matrices available from Linotype and Monotype and decor-

[11]

Facsimiles of a number of type-specimens have been made (see below). Comparison is therefore much easier now — a detailed study awaits its author.

the Vatican Press, Hertzberger, 1967
Delacolonge, Van Gendt, 1969
Rosart, Van Gendt, 1973

ative units from the Caslon Letter Foundry
and continental foundries (Stempel, Klingspor
Enschedé, Bauer, Amsterdam, etc.) must run
into several thousands and yet new designs
are cut every year. A new assessment of

available material might be more profitable
than commissioning artists (especially non-
typographic artists) to design contemporary
borders and other decorations. It seems important to the present writer, who is responsible
for the recutting of three designs in this book,
to see that no valuable flowers of the past are
neglected. Rather than cut yet another size of
triangle, square or circle (and every foundry
has cut a whole army of them) the possibilities
of the Stamperia Vaticana acorn might be
examined (see page 34), or the Bauer ornament (≪), designed by E. R. Weiss, might
receive wider recognition. Flinders Petrie recorded this branched leaf at Zygouries, c. 1400
B.C. Similar forms were used as binders'

stamps *c.* 1500. Even the Granjon arabesque, so frequently experimented with, still has untried values and, surprisingly enough, certain basic arrangements ideally suited to the types have suffered neglect. The arrangement shown on the opposite page is not to be found in Frederic Warde's collection and may even be making its maiden appearance.

The cutting of every matrix raises the question: shall it be for exclusive use or put on the open market? Many borders and decorations have been designed and cut for the exclusive use of printers—particularly the Curwen Press and the Fanfare Press—but these do not amount to very much when compared with the untried possibilities of open-market designs.

If the factor of exclusiveness is considered desirable one way of obtaining this, without commissioning and founding copyright material, is by cutting variations on the types themselves. Examples of these hand-cut variations may be seen on pages 24, 30 and 45. With the simplest of tools and techniques, and only a slight experience of how the metal reacts under the cutting-tool, such alterations may be done surprisingly quickly. The Fournier flowers (468-9) each took about 15 seconds to cut.

Typefounders' specimens have probably played an important part in the neglect and abuse of printers' flowers—a reversal of pur-

[13]

Some years after the publication of this book the author had cut for the first time as a fleuron a border design originally cut on wood by Eustachio Celebrino, c. 1517.

The two units involved were cut for the exclusive use of the Stellar Press and since the corner-piece is different from Celebrino's, & was invented by the present writer, it is copyright.

pose which might some day be worth detailed investigation. Certainly no specimen sheets or books known to the present writer do very much towards the proper understanding of the combinable natures of flowers—at least not in a way which is both effective and economic. Specimens produced by Fournier and his imitators in the eighteenth century led printers up a short and difficult path. The fault lay entirely in the way these flowers were used.

The main fault with contemporary founders' and printers' specimens lies firstly in arrangement and secondly in a lack of selectivity. The usual arrangement consists of a numerical list of short strips collectively called borders which are subdivided into point-size groups. And without selection leading to the removal of certain undesirables (starting with those of bad design and inappropriate scale), the more important material remains obscured.

The successful mixing of flowers in the same fleuron group, or on the same page, in part relies on the personal taste of the designer and in part on his acquaintance with historical typography. But what is really needed is a comprehensive knowledge of the combinable natures of a fairly large group of flowers. The following pages are intended as an opening gambit and leave the real subject to be individually pursued.

In this enquiry there are no simple rules to

[14]

follow—so much depends on personal taste and a critical selection of the all-too-vast repertoire available. The question remains: what technique shall be employed in the search for combinable qualities? And the answer may well be that nothing short of arranging and proofing the type units themselves will be really adequate. The present writer has always worked in metal, and established for this purpose a private press in the form of an experimental workshop. Many of the arrangements shown in the following pages would not easily have been discovered by drawing or using tracings or even with the aid of an inkpad and a sort of each flower.

Experiment is particularly rewarding when unexpected qualities of combination reveal themselves as with this ancient unit of Giolito (☙) and this modern unit of Fournier (☞):

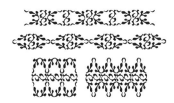

There is also room for a good deal of experimenting with familiar sorts from Monotype letter-founts:

[15]

and with a combination of Linotype and Monotype decorative materials:

⁂⁂⁂⁂⁂⁂⁂⁂⁂⁂⁂⁂⁂⁂⁂

To conclude, it is now only necessary to
throw open the subject for discussion and
experiment, and to say that this book is
intended for the typographer blessed with
imagination and capable of restraint.

suite des vignettes
flowers
fleurons
vignettes
viñetas
ornemants
ornamenten
ornaments
fregi   [16]
röslein
borders
[tarotee] *

*for the backs of
playing cards

THE

SUITE

A booklet called Printers' Ornament by Dale Roylance [Yale University Library, no date] suggests a crude form of vine leaf was used by Aldus Manutius c. 1500, and further developments by Giovanni Padovano, 1528, by Dolet, 1540, and Egenolff, 1590. To these references may be added de Colines, 1542, and many others.

Vine leaves appeared as types early in the sixteenth century—firstly on a Ratdolt title-page dated 1512, and the finer cutting shown above at Paris in 1527. The design shown overleaf (223) was used at Lyon by Jean de Tournes in 1556 and by Jacques Kerver at Paris in 1557.

According to Flinders Petrie these designs existed at Rome in the first century B.C. The Venetian printers Ratdolt and Aldus revived this Roman leaf which was first cut as a binders' stamp and later recut as a printers' flower. The collective name, Aldine leaves, comes from their use on bindings of Aldus, *c.* 1510.

Vine leaves are essentially pointers serving much the same purpose as fists but they may also be used as line finishers or to terminate a tapering design.

[19]

On reading
Flinders Petrie
again, origins
of the ivy
leaf and the
vine leaf
appear to date
from c. 2000
B C in Crete.

MONOTYPE 224 / 8, 10, 12, 14, 18, 24, 30, 36

MONOTYPE 223 / 6, 8, 10, 12, 14, 18, 24, 30, 36

set 15 *units*

[20]

A VENETIAN ARABESQUE

A typical unit of arabesque which, in slightly varying forms, has existed in the East and in Europe for centuries.

As a type unit the design shown here was to be found in the Venetian printing office of Gabriele Giolito in 1552. It has three uses: as a line finisher, as a pointer and as a combinable unit of arabesque pattern. Giolito may have cut his unit after a binder's stamp or possibly adapted it from a design in one of the many books of arabesques already published at that time.

Before the end of the sixteenth century type unit copies made their appearance at other cities in Italy, at Antwerp and at Paris. Lamesle, the Parisian founder, made a recutting in Petit Texte in 1742.

[21]

Whatever the Eastern origins may be, Flinders Petrie quotes examples of the basic forms of arabesque in use in Antrim, c. 250 BC.

GABRIELE

GIOLITO

AT VENICE

1552

MONOTYPE 280 / 8, 10, 12, 14, 18, 24, 36
set 9 units
BAUER 4141 *and* MONOTYPE S4757 (☞)

[22]

Four years after the
appearance of Caflisch's book
(see, overleaf) Elliot Offner
produced at the Rosemary
Press in Northampton, Mass,

Robert Granjon, the talented punchcutter of Paris and Lyon, is known to have worked at Antwerp for Plantin in 1565, and it has been suggested that he cut punches for these type units collectively called 'Granjon's Arabesque' in that city at that time—although perhaps not for Plantin. Guillaume Silvius, who published an arabesque pattern-book in 1554, may have been the first to use them for they appear in his books printed at Antwerp from 1572 onwards.

Two years later, in books printed at Lausanne by François Lepreux, the same fleurons appear, and in 1577 Guillaume Rouillé employed them at Lyon, an acknowledged centre of fleuron founding. Their use is recorded at Rheims in 1582, at Rome in 1590, and at Heidelberg in 1597. It is known that Granjon worked in Rome in 1588 and it might be supposed

a book of 30 arrangements of the Granjon arabesque. His asymmetric and unorthodox use of the flowers was done in a blaze of colour far more ambitious and successful than Warde's book of 1928. Officer's book is something *of a rarity since only 250 copies were printed.*

that he retained possession of the punches (originally cut at Antwerp?) and that he subsequently sold strikes in Lausanne, Lyon, Rheims, Rome, Heidelberg and other cities.

Woodcut copies in imitation of certain arrangements of these type units appeared in London during the latter half of the sixteenth century.

The complete arabesque comprises six separate designs (*see page 26*) and has yet to be surpassed for its beauty and ingenious versatility.

* * *

Variety of arrangement is increased by cutting away parts of the design. Each of the 12 units below is modified slightly.

[24]

This arrangement, at the tail of p 24, with its actual cuts in the metal, is a tribute to Sir Francis Meynell in whose edition of In Memoriam it first appeared (1933).

· ·

· ·

[25]

It has recurred, for instance,
in Max Caflisch's book,
Kleines Spiel mit Ornamenten,
Bern, 1965

MONOTYPE 310 MONOTYPE 313
24 x 24 pts.   24 x 6 pts.

MONOTYPE 666 MONOTYPE 665
24 x 21 pts.   24 x 21 pts.

MONOTYPE 311 MONOTYPE 312
24 x 24 pts.   24 x 24 pts.

A NEGLECTED ARABESQUE

These units of arabesque appeared in Chr. Plantin's *Index Characterum* of 1567 in the setting of a complicated fleuron group using 12 different sorts. The same designs, used in a similar way, appeared on Konrad Berner's specimen sheet issued at Frankfort in 1592. As printed above the units also appeared on Berner's specimen at the ends of an arabesque strip from which the Linotype recutting (below) was made.

Its use in the building of larger arabesques seems to have obscured the integral value of this flower which may have been cut by Granjon.

LINOTYPE 272-5 / 18

The two units, as shown at the head of this page, appeared on Anton Janson's Leipzig specimen of 1678, again merely as an endpiece, but this time to an entirely inappropriate set of flowers. Sixty-four years later these Antwerp flowers reappeared in Lamesle's specimen of 1742 where the particular arabesque in question, a very poor recutting, was printed in groups of four units. The slight enlargement reproduced by line block below shows that the

cutting was shaded as were the original flowers on Plantin's specimen.

The experimental Monotype recutting shown here has been made from Konrad Berner's sheet but with solids in place of shaded portions and with the simple leaf rendered open. It has yet to be decided, for the final version, whether or not this leaf would appear more appropriate as a solid (*see block below*).

[28]

The Question must be considered as somewhat academic & maybe moribund since 20 years have elapsed & it remains unanswered!

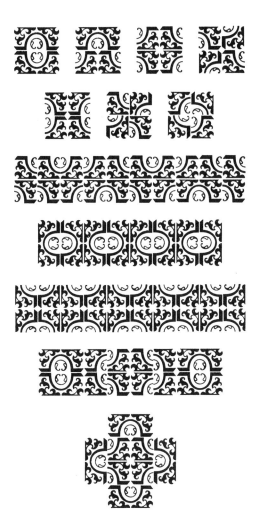

[29]

MONOTYPE 1294-5 / 18 *set* 18 *units*
Modified sorts and arrangements with
240 / 36 *and* 219 / 18

—this fleuron was used
with elegance at Cambridg
in *Bruce Rogers & America*
Typography [30]   by John
Dreyfus, 1959.

A LYONNAISE ARABESQUE

Lyon, according to Baudrier's *Biblio-graphie Lyonnaise*, was the place of origin of Granjon's arabesque and although this may not be true that city was certainly a centre of fleuron founding in the six-teenth century.

Guillaume Rouillé, who had worked with Giolito in Venice, opened his own printing office at Lyon. It may be that Rouillé or Pierre Roussin, perhaps with aid from Salomon or Granjon, cut this arabesque about 1570. François Lepreux used it four years later at Lausanne.

Some of the eighteenth century foundries recut this unit. Lamesle (1742) issued an alternative with the design cast vertically. Using the diagonal casting only, the nature of this flower gives it many advantages over those of Aluise and of Giolito (*see overleaf*).

MONOTYPE 219 / 8, 10, 12, 14, 18, 24, 30, 36

set 18 *units*

WITH 274-5 & 467

see pages 46-7

[32]

GRANJON'S ACORN

Acorns date back to *c.* 1520 in France as binders' stamps and are to be found in a woodcut border printed at Venice in 1478 by Ratdolt. A more stylised acorn became common on German playing cards about 1480.

This acorn may have been first cut as a type unit by Robert Granjon. A Plantin specimen of Granjon's Petite Antique, dated 1570, includes the acorn seen above and so does the Egenolff specimen of 1592. (Jacques Sabon of the Egenolff foundry worked at Antwerp for Plantin and met Granjon there in 1565).

The Stamperia Vaticana specimen of 1628 contains two varieties of acorn— one with a solid cup and the other with a pattern of white dots on the cup. The solid-cup acorn has a continuous curve throughout the stem & fruit, a subtlety of design which did not appear in the 1570 Antwerp specimen and which unfortunately

[33]

Some research might be usefully continued amongst early woodcut initials — for Plantin, for instance. Stephen Harvard's recent study Ornamental Initials, New York, 1974.

does not recur in later cuttings. Many bastard shapes (like No. 24 in Mozet's specimen of 1743) appeared in the eighteenth century and were perpetuated into the twentieth century.

Its uses are as limited as those of the vine leaf and yet the curved design from the Vatican specimen of 1628, with a reversed (left-to-right) companion, might have proved as interesting in combination as Fournier's oblique-cast flower which is described in a later section.

MONOTYPE 267 / 6, 12, 18, 24, 36
set 14 *units*
Exceptions: 12 x 9 pts & 36 x 27 pts

[34]

In the Vatican specimen on pp 7 & 60 other flowers are shown. But for these the acorn is the only design used — and appears only in headings as a pointer.

A NUREMBERG ARABESQUE

The heirs of Johann Andrea Endter of
Nuremberg issued a book on printing in
1733, *Die Wol-eingerichtete Buchdruckerey*,
containing specimens of flowers used by
Endter in his printing office *c.* 1721. One
of these flowers was the arabesque printed
above. In the same specimen this flower is
also shown cast obliquely on a smaller body.
Probably Endter was not the first printer
to use this particular design which Rosart
recut for Pfeiffer of Amsterdam in 1752.

Stamps of the 'Unicorn' binder, who
worked at Cambridge in the late fifteenth
century, closely resemble Endter's arabesque which is more useful as a single
piece of decoration than as a combinable
unit of pattern. As the contemporary
counterpart of a *petit fer* it has been used
on publishers' bindings by the Nonesuch
Press in 1935 and by Phoenix House in
1954. The latter publisher cut a larger,
open version in 1955.

[35]

MONOTYPE 240 / 36

set 18 *units*

WITH FOURNIER STAR

see page 48

LOUIS LUCE'S FLOWERS

Louis Luce, the third punchcutter of the Imprimerie Royale, issued his miniature type specimen of eight leaves containing several ornaments and flowers in 1740. A few of these were adapted and improved by Fournier whose first (12mo) specimen appeared two years later.

Luce, however, showed considerably more interest in cutting larger ornaments as an economic replacement of woodcut vignettes and borders. His *Essai d'une nouvelle Typographie*, printed by Barbou in 1771, demonstrates this and by about that date Caslon, Fournier, Lamesle, Mozet, Gando, Enschedé, Wetstein, Briquet, Trattner and Delacolonge had already produced a vast repertoire of flowers.

Sunray designs, with and without faces, are to be found in fifteenth century woodcuts and bindings but doubtless their origin may be dated amongst the earliest forms of decoration. Possibly Luce cut the first sun (*fleur de luce*) as a type unit and Fournier copied it a year or two later.

Four of the designs in the following section may owe their origin to Luce:

although the two cruciform flowers did not appear in Luce's specimen of 1740 and in slightly different forms in the 1771 specimen. The flower and the sunray designs were somewhat crude in the 1740 specimen but may have been Fournier's models.

LUCE   FOURNIER

[38]

Delacolonge,
see overleaf
the
original
size is
Parangon

In the eighteenth century, following
Luce & Fournier, great activity in
flower-cutling was evident. The
range of images went far beyond
the floral and arabesque.

Pierre-Simon Fournier first began to cut punches for his own typefoundry in Paris, *c.* 1736. He died in 1768 having successfully devoted his life to this particular branch of typography, but he died not without some bitterness concerning his constant though fruitless effort to overcome a trade prejudice which denied him the right to print.

For some of the flowers in his first specimen book Fournier drew inspiration from Luce's miniature *Epreuve* of 1740 but the majority of them showed originality and skill. It is interesting to note that he eschewed the splendid vine leaves and arabesques of the sixteenth century.

Fournier's flowers earned him the admiration of the world. His second specimen book, *Modéles des Caractères de l'Imprimerie*, printed by Jean-Joseph Barbou in 1742, contains 118 *vignettes*: his *Les Caractères de l'Imprimerie* of 1764 contains 377 *vignettes* and many of these designs were quickly copied in other European foundries.

[39]

Further study of flowers might relate the appearance of new images to the socio-political life of place and period.

Although deprived of the right to print Fournier nevertheless set some of the formes of his specimen books (in an amazingly complicated fashion) and his followers have, in the main, 'taken leaves out of these books'. It was natural enough for the punchcutter-founder to wish to show the entire repertoire of his skill in a single headpiece but it does not follow that printers would be doing him justice by trying to emulate his examples. In fact it may be possible to pay the greatest tribute through a very different approach as the following pages intend to suggest.

The flower of this section's title, because it is cast obliquely on the typebody, is capable of many variations in arrangement. Its immediate origin may be in a crude little design of Luce but certainly binders' stamps of a similar kind existed in the sixteenth century. As a type it has rarely, if ever, had a chance to show off its potentialities, and so here, in the strips and other arrangements which follow, this silhouette flower makes a very belated début.

[These MONOTYPE designs 475-6 are available in 10, 18, 24 and 30 point sizes, *set 12 units.*]

[40]

A particular new image appearing in Delacolonge of 1773 (facsimile edited by Harry Carter) is of buildings. (see p 38)

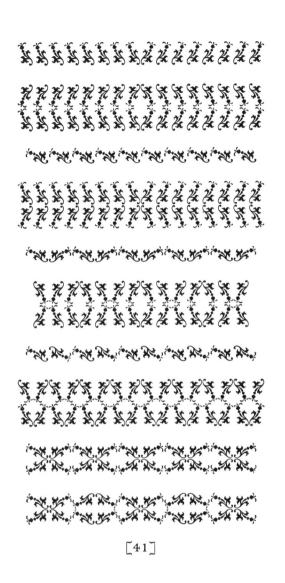

[41]

this seems uncommon
and might be traceable
to some specific use.

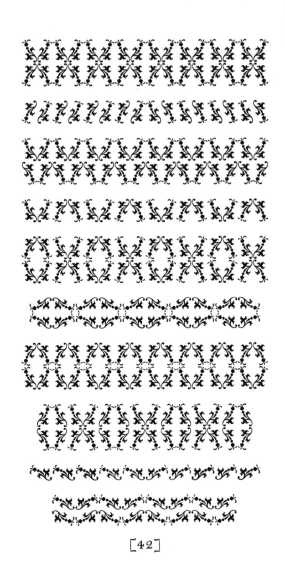

[42]

After examining the versatility of this design in strip arrangement it will not be much of a surprise to see a group of eight units forming a circle or to see the fleurons which arise from an eight-group in combination with the Lyonnaise arabesque shown in a previous section.

6, 10, 12 / set 9 units

This simple design cast obliquely and accompanied by a left-to-right reverse was invented by Fournier. Its value as pattern-builder has scarcely been tried— perhaps because the unit by itself looks quite insignificant. The following list of arrangements may become the basis for experiment but it is important to limit the complexity of arrangement or the use of such decorations will be banned by both

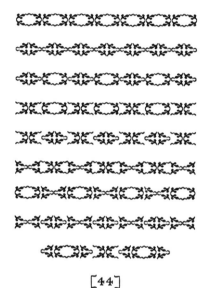

[44]

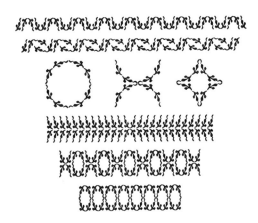

economic and aesthetic considerations. The typographical craftsman should have sufficient experience and skill in his hands to cut with some confidence an alteration on the face of a type. For instance the removal of the 'accent' on this flower (🌸) may be desirable in certain instances although it would not justify the cutting of special matrices.

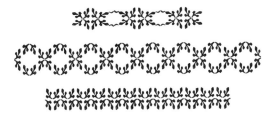

This unit, cast diagonally on a square body, makes the following patterns in the familiar four-group:

It will also combine happily with several other flowers both from Fournier's repertoire and elsewhere (*see page 32*).

MONOTYPE 470 / 10, 12, *set* 9 *units* ⇥
MONOTYPE 271 / 8, 10, 12, 14, 18, 24, 36 ✳
set 18 *units*

[46]

Although cut by Fournier this unit is alien
to his style and it does not appear in the
collection of 141 examples accompanying
his oblong quarto specimen book of 1742.
The unusual placing of the design on the

face and the left-to-right reverse both add
to the versatility of pattern-building.
Four-groups, strips and fleuron settings
shown here give but a bare indication
of 'combinable natures'.

[47]

✳❖✳❖✳❖✳❖✳

MONOTYPE 480 ❖ 8, 10, 12 *set* 15 *units*
AND 1283 ✳ 10 *set* 18 *units*

Since Fournier cut these two types, *c.* 1742,
many copies have been made. Both designs appeared many years earlier—the
oval ornament on a woodcut title-page
printed at Salamanca, *c.* 1496, and later,
on a binding by Geofroy Tory, *c.* 1531,
and the star dates back to a Persian binder's
stamp, *c.* 1580. [A similar star of eight
arms existed at Palaikastro, *c.* 2400 B.C.]
Rosart recut the ornaments for Enschedé
whose specimen of 1748 shows them
printed as a border. It seems likely that
Baskerville, who copied this arrangement,
recut them after Rosart rather than after
Fournier. Another English founder, Isaac
Moore of Bristol, had added both designs
to his stock by 1766.

The flattened oval in the Linotype
version resembles Fournier's original but
a good cutting of the star has not been
available in the present century until recut
by Monotype in 1955.

Johann Thomas Trattner, in his Vienna
specimen of 1760, gives two varieties of
angels' heads (Röslein 11, shown above)
and a smaller, simpler version with hair
in solid black & crudely cut wings whose
tips do not project as in No. 11.

This cruder cutting was shown in specimens issued by Joh. Enschedé in 1744,
by Rosart in 1761, by Amstel in 1767, by
Wilson in 1786, by Unger in 1791, and
by Oomkens in 1807. It is unfortunate that
the crude version should have been so
frequently recut but it may justify at-
tributing the design shown in this section
to Trattner.

Bodoni cut a new design for his specimen of 1771 which shows an alternative
oblique casting.

The angel's head with wings (cherub),
in one form or another, has been commonly
used in woodcut borders and on binding
designs throughout the sixteenth century.

[49]

Meyndert de Winter, in his foundry catalogue produced at Amsterdam in 1744,
offered several *viguren in't hout gesnede*
(some of which appeared in Elzevir's
specimen of 1713). Amongst the woodcut
viguren is a cherub which could have been
Trattner's model.

MONOTYPE 1029 / 18 *set* 18 *units*

WITH MONOTYPE 468-9 / 12

WITH MONOTYPE 675 / 24

[50]

THE DIAMOND SHAPE

The first printers, imitating contemporary scribes, made diamond-shaped marks of punctuation but, after this early start, punchcutters seem to have neglected the diamond as an ornament until the time of Fournier. And even Fournier, with his very great range of *vignettes*, did little more than employ and repeat the basic rhomboid figure as a diapered ground in some of his complicated headbands.

According to Flinders Petrie a shapely diamond contained within an oval has been found in decorative patterns from Ur, about 3500 B.C. and at Cuma, without the oval, *c.* 670 B.C. An Irish book satchel of the eleventh century was stamped with a design similar to the one found at Ur, and several varieties of diamond-shaped stamps are in evidence on Spanish fifteenth-century bindings. From English bindings at the end of the fifteenth century an interesting detail of development is shown as a tail-piece to this section. The first design, a pineapple stamp of 1479, depicts a more or less realistic fruit. The second, of a few years later, shows the pineapple in a

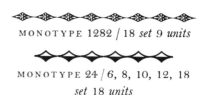

MONOTYPE 1282 / 18 *set 9 units*

MONOTYPE 24 / 6, 8, 10, 12, 18
set 18 *units*

stylized form, whilst in the third, early sixteenth century, the fruit has become a shapely diamond with a flower in reverse.

William Caslon I, in his specimen of 1798, seems to have been the first type-founder to show a diamond of fair shape. He produced three flowers on the English body all with black flowers on white grounds and two of these designs have their diamond-shapes surrounded by dotted ovals—the third retains the dots only at the points of the diamond.

Andrea Amoretti's specimen of 1811 (Parma) shows a simple black on white flower within a finely shaped diamond, &

[52]

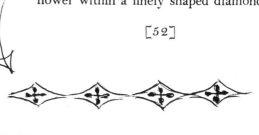

Nicola Pietelli (Bernardo, 1814) used a border of rhomboid units with flowers showing white on black.

In the 1815 specimen of Vincent Figgins the two diamond-shaped flowers shown above first appeared.

ADDENDUM

In 1729 Samuel Palmer of London printed a 'proposal' to publish his *General History of Printing* in monthly parts. In this announcement the neglected arabesque described on page 27 was employed as a simple strip arrangement in groups of 4 units. There is little doubt that Palmer imported his material from Holland.

This same arabesque was in use at the Oxford University Press in the eighteenth century and appeared on a keepsake for Mr John Shepherd, dated 1722.

From Monotype, after publication of A Suite of Fleurons, there followed a series of broadsheets devoted to flower arrangement. There also followed an ingenious little flower

BIBLIOGRAPHY

CARTER, H. G., *Fournier on Typefounding*, 1930
  Letter Design & Typecutting (R.S.A. Journal), 1954
DREYFUS, John, *Baskerville's Ornaments*,
  (Cambridge Bibliographical Society), 1954
JOHNSON, A. F., *The 'Antwerp' Ornaments*,
  (New Mechanick Exercises), 1954
MEYNELL, Francis, *Typography*, 1923
  Typographic Flowers (Signature 7), 1937
  WITH Stanley Morison:
  Printers' Flowers and Arabesques
  (Fleuron No. 1), 1923
MORISON, Stanley
  Monotype Flower Decorations, 1924
  On the Typographical Ornaments of Granjon,
  Fournier and Weiss, 1925
  Venice and the Arabesque, 1955
UPDIKE, D. B., *Printing Types*, 1937
WARDE, Frederic, *Printers Ornaments*, 1928

Dale Raylance, see p 18

Elliot Offner, see p 23

Max Caflisch, see p 25

Stephen Harvard, see p 33

called "glint" — which had
popularity for a while but
which now rests under the
dust of disuse, happily out
of sight.

A few pages of photographic freedom

On the preceding page the Stephenson Blake flower No. 526 is shown in movement, the image being moved in the enlarger.

 Opposite, the flower image is enlarged from Stephenson Blake's 326/502 and printed on a background made from a magnified out-of-focus image of cotton fabric.

Stephenson Blake's 326/502 using a mirror image repeated and printed in negative with the corner-piece ornament also reversed black to white. The centre image is then printed positive in colour.

Berthold foundry ornament No. 594 here shown as a multiple, superimposed image made in the enlarger. The background photographic detail from a tombstone is reproduced with a line negative tint.

Detail of an enlargement (×45) of Stephenson Blake's flower No. 328/50c with a smaller enlargement of the complete image printed at the centre and reversed out of the background where the two images coincide.

Negative mirror image of an arrangement of
Monotype ornaments Nos. 246 and 295 shown
below and (opposite) Haas typefoundry unit
No. 2996, a detail shown enlarged approximately
× 20. Note the effect of paper grain on the
edges of this image.

A detail of Stephenson Blake's border unit
No. 51c enlarged. The negatives and positive
plates were each made from a toned negative.

A multiple image of Monotype No. 1038 from an enlarged toned negative. The endpapers of this book use this multiple image in reverse.

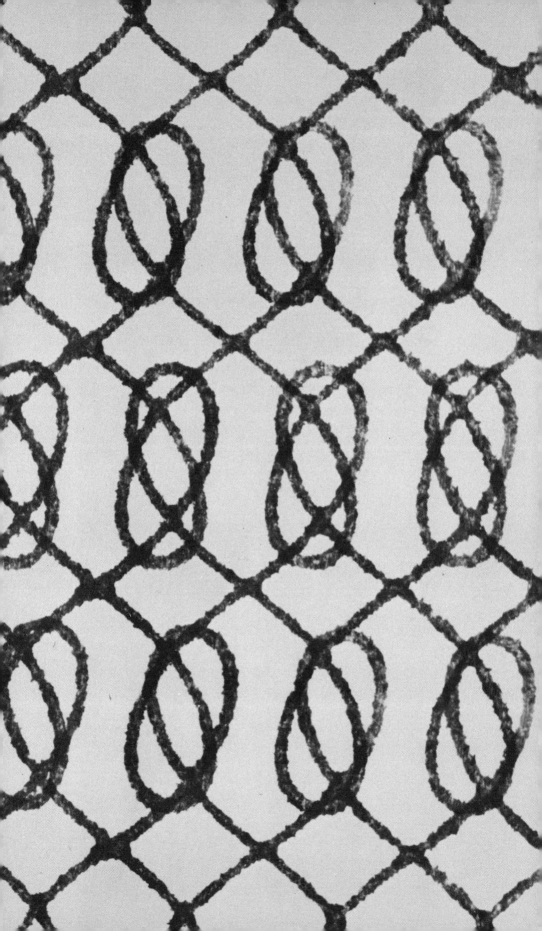

Multiple photographic mirror
images of Monotype No. 224
shown here in different
enlargements.

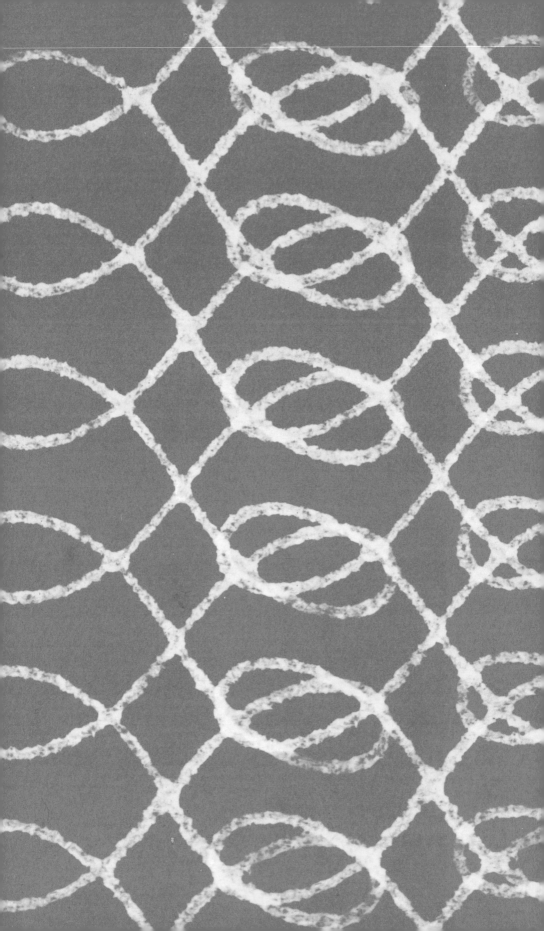